LET ME DIE

LET ME DIE

A study of voluntary euthanasia
containing many case histories

LLOYD COLE

Lloyd Cole

Maidenhead, 1992

First Published 1992

Lloyd Cole
37 College Avenue
Maidenhead, SL6 6AZ, UK

© in this compilation, Lloyd Cole, 1992

ISBN 1 874052 10 7 hb
1 874052 11 5 pb

A Cataloging in Publication Data record
is available from the British Library

Printed in Great Britain by Billings Bookplan Limited

CONTENTS

DEDICATED TO ALL WHO CARE

INTRODUCTION

In the preparation of this book I have been assisted by the Voluntary Euthanasia Societies (VES) of England, Scotland, Australia, New Zealand and the United States of America.

I have tried to show why it is necessary for voluntary euthanasia to become lawful. There is no argument strong enough to justify continual and unending misery and pain. If there is a crime, it is to take away the dignity of a human being, not to protect and preserve it.

I would encourage all who believe in the cause of the severely handicapped or mentally ill, to join the Voluntary Euthanasia Society. At the same time, if in fear of increased and unbearable pain in the near future, it is advisable to complete and sign an advance directive.

I cried several times as I wrote this book and read again of the suffering, love and courage of others. I hope the reader will feel the pull of the greatest love, and be willing to risk life to bring release from misery to others.

Lloyd Cole,
March 1992

1

THE ARGUMENT

What argument? It could be said there is no argument. If the continuance of suffering is evil then the cessation of suffering must be good. If there is no way to correct an evil state it may well be thought that to eliminate the state is a blessing.

No one allows a dog or a horse to continue suffering if there is no remedy for the suffering. To have a dog put to sleep is regarded in such circumstances as a kindness and by no means an evil or wicked act.

People who are terminally ill, may sometimes be described as cabbages. They may be unable to move or speak, or to recognise a harried loved one. Is there an argument for keeping such people alive against their will, once there is no chance of recovery? As well as the suffering of the terminally ill, one must also consider the suffering of the loved ones. It seems to me that many more than one has to suffer needlessly.

Life is precious, but what is life? Is a cabbage alive?

Sterne once said, "I live in a constant endeavour to fence against the *infirmities* of ill health." In normal living one has to care for oneself. A certain amount of illness is likely for all, and the wise behave in the way most likely to avoid illness. This normal everyday fight against ill health is far removed from the cabbage-like state against which a fight is not likely to succeed.

When pain is constant and the normal behaviour of the living is no longer possible it is difficult to believe that a merciful ending could ever be described as a crime.

Anyone in the condition described as like a cabbage might well re-echo the words of Walt Whitman when he said, "Come lovely and soothing death." Why try to make a future where none exists? Why sanctify pain and suffering?

Modern medical science has done much to overcome pain and to restore the sick to health and strength. A special remedy is needed when the very competent medical profession can do no more. I see no harm in a little help out of a worthless existence and in this the medical profession can be of assistance.

Those interested in how the terminally ill feel, and how their loved ones are driven almost out of their minds by the unnecessarily continued suffering of the one so dear to them, should read *Last Wish* by Betty Rollin.

Betty Rollin writes of the suffering of her mother, and her own torment. Her mother suffered from a malignant ovarian cancer and went through six courses of chemotherapy. After this treatment Betty's mother rallied for a time but then began to lose weight, and became so weak she could hardly stand. The pain was constant and almost unbearable.

Her mother wanted to die. She was ready to die and longing to die, but she did not die. Her life, eventually, was nothing but pain. More and more morphine was administered to reduce the pain or, at least, to control it. Betty saw her mother coming out of morphine hazes, praying for death. A further course of chemotherapy was prescribed. Constant nausea followed. When Betty asked if it was going to be like this always, she was told, "Yes, and worse."

Betty's mother, in great and constant pain, asked, "Who does it benefit if I die slowly? If it helped my children I'd be willing, but it does not do anybody any good."

There is no point at all in a slow death. It isn't life. It's better to die.

Although her mother asked to die, Betty did not know how to help. Ultimately, she helped her mother to take enough pills to slip out of life. There was nothing else a loving daughter could do.

How much agony can a loved one be asked to watch? How much loss of dignity can a son or daughter be asked to observe?

What is the point of this unnecessary suffering? It may suit religious zealots, but nobody else. There is no benefit in such misery.

In Canada a 25 year old woman suffered for 30 months from the ravages of a disease from which there is no hope of recovery. Hearing that she would be allowed to die she smiled through her pain. Doctors said her death would be more or less painless when her respirator was disconnected. Such is mercy, and mercy is beautiful. To quote William Shakespeare:

> No ceremony that to great ones 'longs,
> Not the king's crown, nor the deputed sword,
> The marshall's truncheon, nor the judge's robe,
> Become them with one half so good a grace
> As mercy does.

I have a liking for the expression *mercy killing*. I believe in mercy killing. There may be some dangers in allowing mercy killing, but there is less suffering, less misery, less degradation than in a lingering, tortuous keeping "alive". Let Cowper speak:

> The clouds ye so much dread
> Are big with mercy, and shall break
> In blessings on your head.

To one who has been for a long time in unremitting pain, death is a blessing and a mercy. Edmund Bentley said "There is a great deal to be said for being dead." After all, we say that all good things must come to an end. Why then should bad and evil things go on for ever? To quote the bard of Avon again, why "grunt and sweat under a weary life." Weariness is a bore to be avoided. How much more should constant, unbelievable pain be relieved? Charles Dickens causes Mr Pecksniff to say, "Charity and Mercy. Not unholy names, I hope." *To show mercy is to be numbered among the caring. To prolong, by law, the miserable existence is a crime.*

Preserving life should continue only as long as the life is worth preserving.

Who says life should be preserved at all costs? Outstandingly, the church, and particularly the Roman Catholic church. Why should anyone listen to the church? For many years now the English established church has been discarding one doctrine after another, holding on to very little of the original faith (in contrast to the Roman Catholic church who refuse to change one jot). Very little notice can be taken of the Church of England. This established religion varies in belief from archbishop to archbishop and cannot call for any consistent faith. The Roman Church has always held doctrines that have been to the detriment of the people, and deserves praise only for stubbornness.

While calling people to the light, the church does all it can to preserve the total darkness of superstition and prejudice. Let me revive the call, "Let my people go."

Gray refers to those who "shut the gates of mercy on mankind." Anyone who denies mercy to the suffering is to be condemned, and ignored. This must apply to religious teachers and law givers alike. It is my strongly held view that governments should have nothing to say as to the maintenance of life under great distress and suffering. Precautions to avoid murder for reasons of greed must be maintained. Surely, the medical profession could undertake the necessary control as in the case of abortions. Nobody insists that I should have no money because someone might try to take it from me. The terminally ill must not be asked to continue to suffer in case some people might take life for the wrong motives.

Listen to Portia:

The quality of life is not strained,
It droppeth as the rain from heaven
Upon the place beneath:
It is twice blessed; It blesseth him that gives and him that takes.

To show mercy is the greatest goodness. There must be times when to bring an end to a miserable life is a mercy to be applauded. After a loved one's death the one remaining might well say with Shakespeare "After life's fitful fever he sleeps well."

Anything is better than, as Milton says, "To live life half dead, a living death." The facts have to be faced as they are, not as they might be. If a loved one is in a state of severe suffering over a long period, and there is no hope of recovery, something must be done to relieve the situation. That is mercy, not murder.

What is the argument?

The standard of living has greatly improved over the years. People live longer. For this reason they may suffer more. In these circumstances the doctors often can prolong life although unable to cure. This can mean considerable avoidable suffering. More people are kept alive with incurable and disabling diseases. Many very severe cancers and viral diseases leave people with a long debilitating disability. Such people become totally dependent, unable to do anything very much for themselves. Something has to be done for those people whose suffering is beyond endurance.

Euthanasia conveys a good death. That is what it means. Natural death we all know and accept. Voluntary euthanasia is voluntary death. Death induced to avoid more suffering or a near-death sort of existence. Voluntary euthanasia allows for a distress-free and dignified death. Such can be self induced or assisted, following the express wish of the person concerned.

Following accidents or very sudden severe illness it may not be possible for the ill person to volunteer for death. In such cases I think the medical profession in co-operation with relatives ought to be able to induce death.

The concern is for the rights of all persons in terminal stages of an illness to be able to obtain the relief they desire, and so to avoid continued distress and suffering for which there is no remedy. Those whose lives have no longer any meaning or purpose should be free to escape into oblivion.

It should be possible to obtain medical assistance in terminating life in response to carefully and freely made decisions and directions. When such medical assistance is denied, sufferers may make attempts at suicide which can cause great distress to loved ones. Also, attempted and successful suicide is expensive to society because of the investigations that have to take place. Police and coroners courts become unnecessarily involved at considerable expense.

The medical profession should be permitted by law to administer drugs, or to advise methods of suicide under controlled conditions. Conditions could eliminate any coercion or other ungracious act.

The voluntary euthanasia societies of the world express matters so – the aim is to promote legislation which entitles any person suffering extreme pain or distress, with no reasonable prospect of recovery, to a painless and dignified death in accordance with his or her express directions. Summarised, this means *dying with dignity*. To obtain a change in the law it is important that sufficient people should be in sympathy with the objectives of the voluntary euthanasia societies of the world. The public should surely accept that persons in deep distress with no hope of a cure should be treated with compassion and their wish for a quick and dignified death respected.

It must be clearly stated that a call for voluntary euthanasia does not imply any acceptance of suicide undertaken in fits of depression or the like. The concern is with any proven loss of the quality of life to such a level that life is no longer worth living. It is contended that patients have the right to choose whether they continue to live in agony or not, to choose anything in preference to a living death.

In this connection I have received the following information from the Voluntary Euthanasia Society of South Australia.

There is one act, the South Australian Natural Death Act of 1983, which requires a doctor to cease treatment of dying patients who, though

no longer competent to refuse treatment, have previously made deposi-
tions declaring their wish for cessation of treatment in such circum-
stances. The right of refusal of treatment, even if treatment is needed to
sustain life, would also be protected in a bill brought before the Victorian
parliament in early 1988 as a result of a lengthy enquiry into the right
to die by a parliamentary committee in Victoria. The bill also proposes
to provide that the powers of guardians, and also the enduring powers
of attorney, i.e. powers which survive the loss of competence of the donor,
may cover refusal of medical treatment of this kind. This bill was passed
in August 1990 and it confirms that people may confer such a power
on their agents to come into effect if or when they lose the ability to refuse
treatment on their own behalf. There exists some legislation, and more
is proposed, regarding informed consent and refusal of treatment generally.

The various societies can give advice to members in distress but
are not qualified to give information which could be held as
encouraging suicide. Such could lead to prosecution and possible
conviction on certain charges. It must be stressed that the societies
wish to prevent suicides by distressed or depressed people. The
societies nevertheless believe that people have the right to reliable
information on the topic of suicide as on any other subject.

Back to the opening question of this chapter – are there any
worthwhile arguments against euthanasia? Many arguments put
forward spring from ignorance of the aims of the societies
promoting the need for voluntary euthanasia. One argument is
that once the absolute forbidding of killing is overturned, the state
could feel free to get rid of anybody unwanted, criminal or
disruptive to the government. There is obviously no similarity
between an individual making a choice regarding their own life
(which is to be commended) and, for example, the murder of
unwanted persons by the Nazis. Allowing people to make decisions
regarding their own life or death is not to condone murder.

There is also the argument that voluntary euthanasia would
make it easy for corrupt persons to achieve the death of anybody
they did not want to continue living. Greedy relatives, it is said,

could pressurise elderly relatives to ask to die. Legislation could protect against coercion or fraud. Surely any act of voluntary euthanasia would be attested by doctors, relatives, and the persons themselves. As things are at the moment, decisions to stop treatment or to provide high risk pain-killing drugs can be made without consulting the wishes of the patient.

The Voluntary Euthanasia Society in England provides help to members who wish to make out an *advance directive* to indicate to their doctor what they wish to happen in the event of there being no reasonable prospect of recovery from serious illness. The doctor is not asked to do anything contrary to existing laws. It helps the doctor to a decision on the necessity or not to prolong life. The doctor must benefit from the decision of the patient, given earlier when in full possession of his or her faculties. The patient can ask to decline life sustaining drugs in certain circumstances and/or to receive all needed drugs to alleviate intolerable distress.

Such advance directives cannot be legally binding on doctors or other carers as long as voluntary euthanasia is not legalised. However, many doctors will place an advance directive in the patient's file, and the existence of such a document may influence the decisions of medical staff when cessation of life-sustaining treatment or the making available of high risk pain killers may be lawful options.

Probably Holland is the most advanced country regarding voluntary euthanasia. In the USA courts have recognised a patient's right to refuse treatment. There are very active voluntary euthanasia societies in England and Scotland. Germany, France and Canada have growing societies. There are societies in Australia and New Zealand. Everywhere in Europe there are increasing majorities in favour of voluntary euthanasia being legalised.

Meantime, all can make an advance directive. Remember that the law upholds a citizen's right to refuse treatment including life-sustaining drugs.

The advance directive form should be filled in and witnessed by two persons who are not relatives or not likely to benefit from

the patient's estate. These same witnesses could give evidence as
to one's state of mind when signing. A doctor could be one of
the witnesses. Once filled in, one copy of the directive should be
given to your doctor, one retained and one given to a person likely
to protect your interests. A copy of the advance directive form
issued by the Voluntary Euthanasia Society in England is printed
in Chapter 22.

In this chapter I have mentioned arguments against euthanasia
and dealt to some extent with the pro argument ... there is
more to be said in favour, especially to reiterate that all have the
right to choose to live or die. The Voluntary Euthanasia Society
in England was formed in 1935 under the presidency of Lord
Moynihan of Leeds, past president of the Royal College of
Surgeons.

The main purpose of the society is to influence legislation which
would give any adult person, suffering from any severe illness, and
with no possible known relief available, to receive an immediate
painless death if this is their expressed wish.

Long ago people died quite early from disease. Nowadays,
advances in medical science, medicine, and surgery have made
it possible to maintain life even when it is not a worthwhile life.
However, there must be a time when the continuance of so-called
life is not wished for.

Ludovic Kennedy has written:

*The whole business of euthanasia would be much less a subject for topical
discussion if it had not been for the enormous advance in medical
science – the invention of drugs, the spare part surgery – which has
prolonged life far more than nature intended.*

It can be contended without fear of contradiction from any
sensible person, that it is the quality of life which is important,
not its length. A member of a voluntary euthanasia society,
crippled and in awful and constant pain from chronic rheumatoid
and osteo arthritis, described in a letter her feelings as she

looked ahead to the time when she might be forced to end her life:

What I would really like would be for a doctor to help me. Then I could put it off 'till the last moment, and I know it would be done success-fully. As it is, I shall have to do it secretly, alone, and with the risk of making a dreadful mess of it. I'm making life as good as possible. I'm working very hard at it, but eventually I would like the help I would need to have a good death, as I'm trying to have a good life.

The distress to loved ones in seeing the suffering of one who is longing to die is dreadful, as expressed by Ludovic Kennedy:

My mother was for the last year or so of her life bedridden, had painful arthritis, had cateracts and couldn't read .... She said to me when she was 83 and in a nursing home, "I've had a wonderful life" – and she had too, she'd enjoyed it enormously – "but it's over now and I don't wish to go on with it. I long for death and I can't have it."

Even among the highly religious is a trend towards voluntary euthanasia as illustrated by the Reverend Lord Soper when he said:

I see no conceivable reason why people should be so anxious to keep a piece of mechanism ticking over when in fact the logical and reasonable process of life is already ebbing to a close in this world and entering, as I firmly believe, in another world altogether.

In Britain, in 1985, a National Opinion Poll found 72 per cent of those asked said they believed the law should allow adults to find an immediate and peaceful death if suffering from an incurable physical illness that is intolerable to them, and have previously asked for such help in writing. All ages and religious persuasions, including Roman Catholics, favoured voluntary euthanasia.

The medical profession, also, are showing increasing interest in both the ethical and practical problems connected with voluntary euthanasia. The British Medical Association reported with great interest the present situation in Holland where doctors are not prosecuted for helping their terminally ill patients to die.

Any reader wanting more information will find addresses of voluntary euthanasia societies in Chapter 21.

Closing this chapter, let's say with Edward Parker:

> *Life's race well run,*
> *Life's work well done,*
> *Life's victory won,*
> *Now cometh rest.*

2

A FUNDAMENTAL RIGHT
A view from Australia

In this chapter let us look together at *A Fundamental Right of Every Individual* written by Sir Mark Oliphant, AC, KBE, FRS, FAA of Canberra, Australia in September 1991.

Those who are incurably ill, those who suffer unremitting, intolerable pain, those who realise they are losing their memory and their ability to look after themselves; those who have lost control of their bodily functions through disease or accident; and many others who hate to be a burden on others, may seek death as an end to their miseries. The law allows them to purchase a gun with which to end it all. It permits the sale, often without prescription, of drugs which, taken in excess, will bring an end to life.

Suicide by drowning, hanging, jumping off a high place, cutting one's wrists or otherwise bleeding to death, inhaling carbon monoxide in the exhaust gas of a car engine, wandering off into the bush or desert to lie down and die – all these are not crimes, though they are messy, creating unpleasant problems for those who discover the dead body. An unsuccessful attempt to end one's life is not a crime. Yet, if in the exercise of human compassion, a doctor, nurse, priest or any other person, provides the means of suicide, or assists suicide in any way, he or she risks criminal prosecution.

I am an old man in my 90th year. I live in continual fear that I might suffer an injury which would make me a chronic invalid, that Alzheimer's disease might take charge of me without awareness, that accelerating debilities of old age might leave me dependent on others, or that loss of memory could rob me of all that I cherish in life. If I can no longer enjoy the haunting beauty of the Flinders Ranges, or experience that feeling of oneness with life, and with the whole of nature, which is mine in the endless desert, I shall not wish to remain alive. As a man of science I know what to do if I am conscious. I have left instructions that in the case of injury or illness I am not to be kept alive unless I can subsequently lead a full and satisfying life alone. I hope that the medical profession, and others who may care for me temporarily, will respect my wishes.

I shall continue to advocate the legislation of voluntary euthanasia as a fundamental right of every individual.

In both western and Australian culture there is a taboo on discussing death. Medical practice is all conditioned towards the maintenance of life and the denial of death. The Netherlands has developed a more healthy attitude towards medically assisted dying. This was as a result of propaganda by the medical profession themselves.

Euthanasia can be achieved actively or passively. In the case of active voluntary euthanasia a peaceful death is brought about by medical assistance. In passive voluntary euthanasia death is achieved by the withdrawal of medical treatment. The medical practitioner will be greatly assisted by a notice directing a doctor to refrain from certain medical treatment under specified conditions. This directive should be in writing, signed and duly witnessed at a time when the person is fully responsible for their actions.

The aim is to make lawful a medical procedure which is already taking place. Voluntary euthanasia should be an acceptable procedure in medical practice, an option for patients who need and ask for it.

It is surely accepted that in a democracy individuals have the right to make their own decisions on matters which concern them. The way one dies is such a right. There is no doubt that voluntary euthanasia should be made lawful, and it is impossible to see why it should be deemed unlawful.

There is more to life than the beating of a pulse. To be alive is to be aware. To be alive is to be able to communicate with others, and to have a conscious identity as a person. When such abilities have gone, life is devoid of meaning. No one should be forced to prolong his or her dying. All patients who suffer should receive quick and painless relief. Compassion for the suffering is an accepted principle in all Christian countries. It is contended that this compassion should not be denied to those who seek merciful release from a half-life. Opinion polls in Australia show increasing support for the legislation of voluntary euthanasia. The 1987 poll by the Roy Morgan Research Centre recorded 74 per cent in favour. In 1990 the figure rose to 77 per cent. The degree of support from church members contrasts widely with that of the official church bodies. Many find voluntary euthanasia consistent with their faith in a loving, caring God.

Medical opinion was tested in Victoria in 1987. A questionaire was sent to two thousand doctors. The question asked was:

Do you think it is sometimes right for a doctor to take active steps to bring about the death of a patient who has requested the doctor to do so?

The result was most convincing as 62 per cent said "yes". All religions returned a majority in favour except Roman Catholics. In the Australian Medical Association, 52 per cent thought that their professional organisation should take a stand similar to that of the medical association in Holland by supporting active voluntary euthanasia in certain circumstances and 60 per cent thought that the law should be changed to meet this concept.

The Australian view is that mercy killing is usually a violent act carried out by a loved one but voluntary euthanasia is a carefully considered exercise of an option in medical practice. It depends what is meant by mercy killing. All killing which relieves unbearable suffering could well be thought of as mercy killing. Removal of legal barriers would allow doctors to respond, according to conscience and professional judgement, to the wishes of hopelessly ill patients without fear of prosecution. Everything possible should be done to hasten the day of liberation.

It must become accepted that prolongation of life at all costs is not the legitimate calling of the caring medical practitioner. In Australia there is a widespread acceptance of passive voluntary euthanasia. The use of "do not resuscitate" orders are accepted.

Turning for a moment to the USA, a court decision recently stated that:

> ... *life sustaining treatment may be withheld or withdrawn ... when ... it is clear that the burdens of the patient's continued life with the treatment outweigh the benefits of that life for him.*

Clearly the same justification should apply to active voluntary euthanasia. It is not right that passive should be acceptable whereas active is unacceptable. If death is the aim, what does it matter whether it is passively or actively achieved? Trying to distinguish between the two will only allow for delay in a final decision. Actually, passive euthanasia could leave the patient with further suffering before death whereas active action would be swift and gentle.

No social reform is entirely free of risk and all human enterprise, of whatever kind, is subject to possible error. In the Netherlands voluntary euthanasia is widely practised under safeguards insisted on by the courts. This means that doctors who respect the safeguards will not be punished even though the practise of voluntary euthanasia is still illegal. Six thousand or more patients are receiving medical assistance in dying.

Safeguards suggested by the Doctors Reform Society in Australia are:

- Only doctors may carry out euthanasia.
- Individual doctors may refuse to carry out euthanasia.
- There must be a specific request by the patient which leaves no room for doubt regarding the patient's desire to die.
- The patient's decision must be well informed, free and enduring.

- There is no acceptable alternative for the patient to improve his condition.
- The doctor must exercise due care in making a decision and consult another independent medical practitioner.

Passive voluntary euthanasia is now widely practised in many countries, including Australia, without moral censure and free of legal regulations. In Australia it is not illegal to commit suicide. However, it is a criminal offence to assist someone to do so, punishable by 14 years imprisonment.

Literature I have received from the Euthanasia Society in Australia concludes that there is much suffering by those for whom life has lost its quality. There is also great anxiety among those who fear the suffering and indignity which may come. There is a general acceptance in the community of the principle of voluntary euthanasia but the law is lagging behind. The law needs changing.

Sir Edward Coke has said, "How long so ever it hath continued, if it be against reason, it is of no force in law." Meredith refers to "The unalterable law." While passing, note that the Bible says "He that loveth another hath fulfilled the law". Cromwell said, "Necessity has no law". Sir John Powell said, "Nothing is law which is not reason." I rest my case.

3

A DIGNIFIED END?

The following letters were received at the office of the Voluntary Euthanasia Society of Scotland and arranged in a booklet by Sheila Little in 1989.

From Lady W. in Australia:

After my husband's surgery for removal of the entire ascending intestine and most of the stomach – and having been advised by the surgeon that his type of cancer was likely to recur within five years, when there could be no further surgery or medication – I contacted the New South Wales Society, our intention being to enjoy life to the hilt as long as we were able and then, when it struck again, to quietly go together, as we have no wish to be parted after 45 years of loving partnership.

But our problem was what to take, how to acquire it and the correct amount – so that there could be no blunder. So we turn to you for advice and help, so that our minds can be set at rest with the assurance that my husband will suffer no more pain or indignity and we can slip away peacefully.

Who could resist such a love letter?

From A. McH. of Scotland:

I am afflicted with motor neurone disease, only able to move slowly with a Zimmer as legs severely affected. I have no balance. Situation worsens weekly and I foresee the time when I will be a living vegetable …. It would ease my mind considerably to know that when the time comes I could quietly fade from the scene.

How can it be correct to keep such a man alive once he becomes a vegetable?

From Miss Alice T. of Edinburgh:

... I intended to choose the time of my death. I have done so and hope to suffocate while unconscious from sedative ... I don't choose to risk being trapped into a wheelchair or a hospital bed for the rest of my life.

From Dr Eric V. of Portugal:

> *In memory of an Afghan hound*
> *His sign was gracefulness. His silver coat*
> *Flowed in the wind created by his speed.*
> *Age made him gay and slow until he could*
> *No longer stand. My needle found his vein*
> *And with a look as of gratitude*
> *He slowly wagged his tail and fell asleep.*
> *Whom shall I ask to work this act of grace*
> *On me, a human being, when the time will come?*

This point was made in Chapter 1. Why do we treat our animals more humanely than our fellow human beings?

From M. I. of Scotland:

I nursed my aunt of 88. I was appalled at what age can do. This aunt had fallen so often and hurt her head that she began to take what amounted to epileptic fits. She urinated, defacated, bled all over the place and I swore I would never allow my children to see me in such a state.

From Dr M. of Edinburgh:

I have held strong views on the right of the individual to decide that death is preferable to lingering physical decay and dependency on others since

I can remember, and I have lodged a statement with my lawyer asking that my views shall be respected where medical treatment is concerned.

There are many doctors who support the call for voluntary euthanasia.

From Mrs F. of Rye:

We now live next door to a doctor whose wife had a stroke 12 years ago. She is unable to communicate with anyone and her face and body are distorted .... At first my son was not too happy about us joining the Voluntary Euthanasia Society ... he wanted to hang on to us as long as possible. So that I could make him change his mind about the society ... I played a trick on him. I told him I needed help with the wheelchair because I wanted him to see the doctor's wife with her twisted features .... So he came with me to the room, and when I turned her round so that he saw her distorted face and body, the shock was too much for him ... I said do you want to come visiting your father and mother and see them like this? He said "no" in subdued tones, "No, you are right. You must go out with dignity."

It is hard to imagine how terrible it is to watch someone suffering unless one actually has done so. Anyone who knows how disconcerting it can be to the healthy to observe very severe illness and its consequences will give assent to voluntary euthanasia.

From Lady S. of Alnwick:

When my husband was terminally ill he shot himself. If the day should come when I feel my time on earth should be finished, I hope to be able to take my own life in a more humane manner.

From Norma D. of Glasgow:

I am a cancer patient ... chemotherapy was not effective and I developed secondary growths during the treatment ... the thought of dying with pain and ulcerating growths horrifies me. I believe that people should be able to end their lives by their own hands when life is no longer worth living ... I have such a fear and dread of the final stages of the disease that I cannot live each day in peace as it comes .... Perhaps you could contact me and give me a little bit of hope that the end of my life need not be prolonged hopelessly and in misery.

From Mrs M. J. of Glasgow:

A patient who does not realise he is going to die anyway may allow himself to suffer unbelievable agony in the belief that the treatment he is receiving will cure him. The torture of dying rapidly from a cerebral tumour may last for only a few weeks – a period too short for a young and hitherto healthy man to take in the incredible certainty that he is going to die, but it is still a period long enough for the near obscenities of the mental and physical pain to last for eternity.

My own husband died like this. The tumour caused the swift deterioration of, inter alia, the ability to pass water. During his last few days in hospital, about two litres of water were dripped into a vein and all retained in his body. His bladder swelled up to reach as far as his ribs, and sideways to his pelvic bones; he screamed if anyone touched him. They pushed about twelve inches (30cm) of a rigid tube, quarter of an inch (5mm) thick, into his penis. It was a long and difficult process; the nurse was sweating and exhausted by the time she got it in, but she had been instructed to do this and the patient's roars of agony were not going to stop her. It didn't succeed in drawing off the water, but they continued to drip more water into him because, "this was necessary to maintain his life." Meantime, the pain in his head was greater, he told me, than he could believe possible without every blood vessel in it exploding. The patient bore all this and more because he was a courageous man, but he was too agitated and confused to think of asking for an end to it all. He was also intimidated by the crisp hospital atmosphere. His last words on earth were "For Christ's sake let me have a pee."

I was with him constantly in a private double room throughout his last four days and nights, and saw it all. I hinted as openly as I could at first, and then asked outright for an end to be put to all this suffering. For about 30 hours I was ignored, placated, not understood, offered tranquillisers and mutely reproached. After a further ten or so hours, he was given a final dose. When he had been in a coma for about five or six hours, a specialist arrived and achieved the miracle of releasing floods of water, but by then of course the patient was not in a position to appreciate this. He died in a pool, in a bed sodden with his urine.

From Joan M. of Paisley:

Both of my parents died of cancer ... my mother died screaming in my arms.

From N. T. of Belfast:

I am watching a beloved aunt die in a hospice. She has cancer. I find it impossible to recognise this "thing" – skin stretched over bones – as someone who cared very much about how she looked. I am shocked that someone should be allowed to go in such a state.

From Doris B. of West Croydon:

My beloved mother had a stroke when she was 65 and over twelve years became a vegetable. I looked after her and you can imagine what it was like to see her deteriorate.

From Violet H. of Granton-on-Spey:

I have suffered from cancer of the spine for twelve long years. Radium makes me so sick. There is now no hope and the doctor recommends a hospice.

To keep an animal in the pain I am suffering would bring down the wrath of all.

My doctor says two months – two more months! And at what cost to one's loved ones forced to witness such degradation. Pain degrades one so. We have the right to die in dignity.

From J. W. of Belgium:

Your organisation is one of the rare ones that strive for a real liberation of mankind, for the abolition of fear, for a humane and honourable passing away without the nightmare of a degrading death.

If we can achieve what you strive for there will be no children haunted by the memory of seeing their father and mother die a horrible death without being able to help them in the way they ask, and feeling guilty for the rest of their lives.

From Mrs Nan L.:

My mother is dying of cancer in hospital … it seems to me they are only prolonging her suffering. I wish to die with dignity and be in control of my destiny and not be dictated to by those of different views, e.g. unnecessary religious zeal!

From Miss L. M. of Argyll:

How enjoyable present life would be if one could be certain that in future one could not be forced to live against one's will.

In 1850 the elder sister of Hector Berlioz died of cancer. He wrote in his memoirs:

My beloved Adele, my other sister, nearly died herself from exhaustion and the horror of watching the long martyrdom … yet no doctor dare have the humanity to end it once and for all with a little chloroform. They do it so as to spare patients the pain of any operation that lasts a few seconds, but they will not consider using it to save them six months of torture, when it is absolutely certain that no remedy, not even time, will cure the disease, and death is clearly the only remaining boon, the sole source of happiness.

4

COMPELLED TO DIE ALONE
Reports from the VES Scotland

The Death of Jeannie Geddes

Jeannie Geddes took her own life during the night of 17-18 June and died peacefully on her own terms, after suffering for some years from arthritis and cancer of the liver. Because of the illegality her doctor could not help her to die and she had to die unaided and alone. She had the courage to make sure her son Colin, who was staying with her, should not be implicated in her death. When the plastic bag was lifted from her head, her face was beautiful in its serenity.

Her loss to the Voluntary Euthanasia Society of Scotland is much felt for she served on the executive committee for some years. By realising what comprised the essential, and by totally lacking any tendency to exaggeration, she was able to see to it that only wise policies were followed. She had great perception. She saw through the insincere. She allowed only what she considered good for the society. The report of her from the Scottish Society says she had "the power to put matters into a few telling and precise words." She used this power to good effect at meetings of the Edinburgh Medical Group where she argued the case for voluntary euthanasia. Eminent medicos who opposed the society could not silence her. She resisted all anti-society speeches and re-emphasised her points with courage and absolute conviction.

Jeannie wrote many telling letters to local and national newspapers. So effective were these letters that they were invariably followed by applications to join the society.

Jeannie was a very generous person. This was demonstrated in 1980 when the society needed funds. Jeannie made an interest-free loan of £5000 until the money started coming in. As the society did not have any premises she allowed her flat to be used for meetings. She baked delicious cakes for the member's teas. All her efforts were made with humility and with obvious enjoyment which constantly inspired the members in difficult times.

Jeannie was not a Scot but born in Montpellier, France. She was very alive and impressed all with her frankness and innocent outlook. However she was not naive, while brimming over with kindness and wisdom.

In 1932 she was married to Arthur Geddes, the son of Sir Patrick Geddes who was the founder of the International College des Ecossais at Montpellier. Arthur Geddes himself became a lecturer in geography at Edinburgh University. The pair lived in Edinburgh but visited India on geographical ventures. Jeannie bore her husband three daughters and one son who were a delight to her, and they were a very united family.

On her husband's death Jeannie devoted herself unselfishly to the needs of others. She helped in many ways, unknown except to those concerned. She served meals on wheels until her arthritis made this impossible. She worked in an Oxfam shop until the end of her life. She supported Amnesty International, Friends of the Earth, the Scottish Council for Civil Liberties, and of course the promotion of voluntary euthanasia was an active interest. Despite all this she enjoyed joining in the musical, literary and artistic life of Edinburgh.

She was very much loved and is greatly missed.

The Death of Ruth Barr

Mrs Ruth Barr, of Perth, dearly loved member of the Voluntary Euthanasia Society of Scotland died by her own hand. She was an American, born in Dallas, Texas in 1903. She enjoyed life to the full and the afternoon before her death enjoyed a joy-ride in an airplane. She had written a letter to her friends which her daughter allowed to be published. This is the letter:

Dear Friends,
When you read this, if my plans are successful, I will no longer be with you on this planet. All the responsibility for this action is mine alone. Betty, my daughter, understands my viewpoint and therefore she will not be surprised (unless by the timing) ... for about twenty years I have thought that an elderly person (I am 87) should feel free to end his or her life on earth. Too many have to face senility, feel pain, depend on others.

What follows is a letter sent to friends by Betty, Ruth Barr's daughter:

On 30 July my beloved mother died ... there is happiness mixed with sadness because she died as she had always wished, peacefully in her own home overlooking the beautiful Perthshire hills .... In recent years she had become active in the Voluntary Euthanasia Society of Scotland and so acted on her principles, thinking that "an elderly person should feel free to end his or her life on earth" as she herself said in a farewell letter to friends. She planned everything meticulously and took an overdose of sleeping pills at a time when we were in Edinburgh. Her physical condition had deteriorated rapidly during the past year, partly due to a neck fracture sustained in a car accident. What touched George and I, in particular, was that she timed her death thinking of us.

5

HELP FROM HIS BEST FRIEND
A case study from New Zealand

From the New Zealand Society for Euthanasia I have received details concerning a best friend who helped a tetraplegic to kill himself. A newspaper reported:

> *At the district court in Christchurch,*
> *Warren Ruscoe, aged 29, a chef, was*
> *CHARGED WITH MURDER.*
> *The police alleged that Warren Ruscoe*
> *HELPED HIS BEST FRIEND*
> *Gregory Richard Nesbit*
> *TO KILL HIMSELF.*

A Nurse Maude Association care-giver agreed in cross examination that Gregory Nesbit was virtually a head with a living brain and personality, but a dead body from the neck down. He could not eat, drink or take medicine without help. From his bed he used a probe to control the television, stereo, light and a burglar alarm.

Nesbit was paralysed when he fractured his neck in a fall while working on a building site in England. He had gone to England to be best man at Warren Ruscoe's wedding. After the accident he was brought home to Christchurch, New Zealand. Ruscoe also came back to New Zealand and visited Nesbit regularly. After hospital treatment Nesbit went to live in a specially equipped home.

Nesbit's mother said that he had told her he did not want to go on living in the state to which he had been reduced. After the funeral, Nesbit's mother said that Ruscoe telephoned to say he "did it".

In the opening account of the prosecution it was alleged that Ruscoe had agreed with Nesbit to assist him to kill himself by ingesting certain tablets. It was said that Ruscoe went to Nesbit's room and initially gave him ten valium tablets and a glass of water. This was followed with 15 more tablets and between 20 and 25 sleeping pills.

After this, said Ruscoe, the two discussed old times, drank a flask of bourbon, and had several cannabis joints. Later Nesbit became drowsy and told Ruscoe to use the pillow. Earlier in the evening Nesbit had made Ruscoe promise he would not leave him until he was dead. Ruscoe had promised this. When Nesbit became unconsious and his pulse was very weak, Ruscoe placed a pillow over Nesbit's nose and mouth until he was apparently dead.

Nesbit's care-giver Christine Jane Tindall said Nesbit was a tetraplegic and could only move his head and shrug his shoulders. On the day in question she gave Nesbit his tablets and took his temperature which was lower than normal. He asked to remain in bed. On returning for duty the next morning the carer found Nesbit dead in bed.

She reported the death, and was then asked by the doctor to check Nesbit's supply of tablets. She found that they and his sleeping pills were missing. Cross examined, she declared Nesbit could do pretty well nothing for himself. He could not even cough or sneeze without help as he had no stomach muscles. She further confirmed that he had a living brain but a dead body from the neck down. From time to time he had told her he wanted to "finish it all".

Before his last discharge from hospital Ruscoe had told his mother he wanted to die. He said he did not want to go on living in his present state. She said she would not listen to such talk. She said further that Ruscoe was her son's best friend and must have been persuaded by her son to do what he did. She felt sorry for Ruscoe. Apparently the two men had been friends for 15 years.

A doctor said Nesbit suffered terribly. His life was a misery and his prognosis showed no hope for the future.

Warren Ruscoe told a detective that after he had helped his friend to take up to 50 tablets and pills, his friend said "Cheers, mate" and thanked him for his help. The case in court was adjourned for some three months. Before this, Mr Evan Begg, a clinical pathologist, gave evidence. He said that it was most unlikely that the quantity of drugs given, even in conjunction with alcohol and cannabis, would have caused death. Asked what part the pillow played, the witness said that the pathologist's report showed the presence of vomit in the upper airways and a great deal of fluid in his lungs. It was not known what had caused the vomiting, or whether it was before or after the pillow was used. The witness said if the pillow was involved in the death it was in association with the vomiting, and not asphyxiation.

Cross examined, the witness further said that it was reasonably possible that the drugs themselves could have induced vomiting and caused Nesbit's death. It was only speculation that the pillow had anything to do with the death.

Eventually, Ruscoe was committed to the High Court for trial. The result was that he was convicted and sentenced to nine months in jail for aiding suicide. The press reported that friends and relatives wept in despair, disbelief, and anger at the verdict and sentence. All had expected him to be set free. Ruscoe was later released on notice of appeal.

When he sentenced Ruscoe, Mr Justice Holland said he had much sympathy with him but the law did not tolerate and could not excuse a person who helped another to take his life.

After his friend was injured, it was Ruscoe who with Christchurch services groups led fund raising to have his friend brought back to New Zealand. Nesbit talked a great deal about wanting to die. Ruscoe tried to talk him out of it, but Nesbit's desire to die a "gentle death with dignity" increased. Finally, Ruscoe could not go on saying no.

The charge of murder against Ruscoe had been withdrawn as Ruscoe's use of the pillow could not be shown to be the operating cause of death.

Mr Justice Holland said the law recognised that life was sacred and the courts could not permit a person to deliberately assist another to take his life. He said there was a need to demonstrate that society, by its laws, did not tolerate such behaviour, although he recognised Ruscoe's offending as of the least blameworthy type.

He said further that he believed Ruscoe was motivated solely by compassion. It was easy to see and understand his grief watching his closest friend who desperately wanted to die. Mr Hampton, speaking for Ruscoe, said, "It was the hardest thing Ruscoe had ever done in his life. Putting aside his natural reluctance he, out of love, out of compassion, and in an act of sublime courage, helped his loved friend."

Mr Hampton said that, after the accident Nesbit suffered, he could only move his head and was consigned to a degrading, humiliating, miserable and painful life. He described himself as a "hunk of meat with a head on top with no future." He constantly repeated that he wanted to kill himself. Mr Hampton referred to a doctor's report that Nesbit was in a high-risk suicide category of spinally injured persons. Nesbit was concerned that he might survive the overdose and asked Ruscoe not to leave him until he was dead. In this connection the matter of the pillow came up. Ruscoe saw his actions as those of love for his friend demanding the merciful release of death from a hopeless life.

Nesbit's mother and relatives did not wish any punishment to Ruscoe. They thought his actions to be entirely laudable, compassionate, and deeply humane.

What sort of world is it, and what sort of law, that demands that no help can be given to the hopelessly disabled. As Browne wrote, "Death is the *cure of all diseases*." To Nesbit, as Coleridge said, "Death came with friendly care," and as Chesterton said, Nesbit, "Drank death like wine."

6

LOVING, CARING CHILDREN

Andrew and Nicola Thompson, who tried to kill their terminally ill mother after she begged them to end her suffering, walked free from court in November 1990. They gave their mother a potentially fatal overdose of a powerful painkiller as she lay dying of cancer in hospital. Nurses revived the patient, who died two weeks later.

The brother and sister admitted the charge of attempted murder. They were conditionally discharged for twelve months by Mr Justice Tudor Evans who said that the offence would normally carry a heavy sentence. He said that he was sure that it was deep attachment and love which the brother and sister had for their mother that led them to act in the way they did.

Mr Justice Tudor Evans further said:

I am also sure that the distress of seeing your mother's suffering was overwhelming for both of you. I accept that she pleaded with you to end her suffering. I also accept that you debated long before you decided to embark on the course you did.

The solicitor acting for the brother and sister read a statement which said:

We are very grateful for the sentence passed. We still believe real justice will only start being done when the law is changed so that terminally ill people will have the right to die.

This case focuses the mind on the fact that it should not rest with the justices sitting in judgement as to whether a citizen can show compassion to loved ones. Had the above case come before a

Roman Catholic judge with strong religious convictions about the sanctity of life, it is doubful if he would have given the same verdict. Further, it is quite undeserved that this mother's children should have to plead guilty to attempted murder when acting out of love and compassion for her. It is unforgivable that any threat of punishment should be held over such loving and caring offspring.

7

THE LAST ACT OF LOVE

A newspaper, in reporting how parents helped their daughter to die, headed the article "Death Pact the Last Act of Love."

The judge at Norwich Crown Court showed compassion for the parents of a multiple sclerosis victim who helped her take her own life as the final act of love.

Richard Johnson and his wife Jennifer were each put on probation for a year after admitting aiding and abetting their daughter Sara to commit suicide. The court heard they sat with 23-year-old Sara for up to eight hours as she lay dying of a drugs overdose. They promised her if she ever took an overdose they would not summon help until she was dead.

Mr Justice Garland told the couple:

It is clear that your daughter had reached the limit of medication and it is also clear that the prosecution were not putting the case that you gave any active assistance to your daughter to end her life.

If you had taken any positive steps to assist her, it would have been my painful duty to impose a custodial sentence on you both.

He said it was clear that the couple "took a negative role in simply not going to your daughter's assistance after she had taken an overdose."

The judge added:

What you did was contrary to the laws of the country whatever the moral or ethical grounds for your actions.

What I therefore propose to do is to make a comparatively short probation order in each case. I am sure you will both benefit greatly from help and counselling.

Earlier the couple held hands and wept quietly in the dock as Mr Colin Woodford, prosecuting, told how Sara developed the crippling disease when she was 18. In November 1986 she attempted suicide but recovered and was admitted to a psychiatric hospital. Mr Woodford said that in April this year Sara was living in a separate annexe at her parent's home but was incapable of doing anything for herself.

The day after the family had returned from a holiday together, a doctor was called to the Johnson home and found Sara lying on her back in bed, clutching her toy panda. Three empty bottles of painkillers and tranquillisers were found nearby. Sara left a suicide note.

Mr Graham Parkins, defending, told the court:

It is impossible to describe the struggle that young girl went through. Her parents had no thought in their minds that they were committing a criminal offence. Even if they had, it would not have mattered. Her parents displayed love and patience beyond reproach. It was the final act of love. They had honoured their promise to her.

8

A FAMILY'S UNSTINTING LOVE

In March 1990 a devoted wife was put on probation for a year at Leeds Crown Court. Her offence was the fulfilling of a promise to her husband that she would help him to kill himself if he could no longer endure any more pain.

Karen Taylor, 38 years old, could not refuse her husband when he asked for an overdose of tablets to escape the suffering of multiple sclerosis. David Taylor was almost blind and limited to a wheelchair. The insistence of his longing for death to overcome a life of pain melted the resistance of his devoted and caring wife, a former nanny, the court was told.

On the last night of his life he went out for a meal with his wife and family. His wife fed him and he drank champagne and wine through a straw until he became so weak he had to be taken home. As he later lay in bed his wife gave him his two sleeping pills. He turned to her and said, "I want the bottle Karen. I have had enough. I have really had enough. I want the bottle tonight."

Mrs Taylor later told police that her husband persisted in his pleas. At 5 a.m. he woke in pain begging for more tablets. Mrs Taylor said she gave her husband two more pills although she did not want to do it as it did not seem right. She said she ran crying out of the bedroom.

She then went back into the bedroom and the look her husband gave her said you've let me down – "I just can't describe the look." She yielded then to his demands for tablets, feeding him 50 tablets with water. She says her husband asked, "Will that kill me?" He took the pills gratefully saying, "I love you, I am sorry to have let you down."

34

Mrs Taylor then gave him 20 painkillers, laying down beside him, taking his hand, cuddling him and saying, "I love you Dave." He died within hours. However, doctors found the cause of death to be broncho-pneumonia which, they said, he had probably contracted one or two days before the overdose.

Apparently the parents of both Mr and Mrs Taylor were present in the house when the overdose was given. They knew of the suicide pact but did not interfere in any way. A district nurse making a regular visit was told by Mrs Taylor's father that his son-in-law was asleep as he lay dying. The nurse went away. He and his daughter were sentenced to two months probation for aiding and abetting a suicide attempt.

Sentencing Karen Taylor, the judge said:

No one can listen, as I have listened, to the tragic history of David Taylor's last year and last days without the deepest sympathy for him and his family. No one can hear, as I have heard, the fearful promise which he exacted from you without appreciating the appalling dilemma in which he placed you. You had either to break the law and assist the death of the man you loved, or you had to break a solemn promise given to that same man. The course which you chose was the one you believed to be the kindest to him and, equally, the course which you knew to be the harshest for yourself.

Mr Justice French said his sentence of probation should not be seen as condoning such offences. He continued:

The court will look with care as to the steps which are necessary in the public interest to be taken in each individual case. Having considered this case with the greatest care, the conclusion I come to is that it would not be in the public interest to sentence you to any formal sentence of punishment.

David Taylor had been overtaken by multiple sclerosis in 1981 at a time when he and his wife were considering beginning a family. He had always been a fit and active man with a happy marriage. He extracted the suicide promise from his wife as his condition deteriorated rapidly. His caring wife gave in to his request for this promise. Her husband constantly and repeatedly spoke of suicide when very depressed by extreme pain. In his last year, Mr Taylor, although six feet (1.83m) tall, became progressively weaker and was racked with pain from muscular spasms. When he died he weighed only seven stone (45kg).

His brain and mind remained intelligent despite his poor physical condition. He was aware of the prognosis and knew there would be increased physical disability and pain, thus increasing dependence on others, and gradual decline until death.

Mr Brian Cox, defending Karen Taylor, said the family had shown "unstinting love and devotion" for the sick man and had tried to discourage him from thoughts of suicide. "What she did was solely for her husband. She was obviously shattered by the distress and pain he was suffering." After the case Mrs Taylor said, "We are glad it is all over and done with. The best outcome is what happened when Dave died where and when he wanted."

9

A DOCTOR ACCUSED

A doctor walked free from the Old Bailey after contending that an injection was *intended to kill the pain, not the patient*. The crown offered no evidence against Dr Thomas Lodwig when it was contended in medical evidence that the doctor intended only to administer a painkiller. Lorry driver, Roy Spratley, 48, died in hospital less than five minutes after Lodwig injected him with a potentially fatal mixture of potassium and lignocaine.

While preparing the injection, Lodwig allegedly told a nurse: "I'm going to send someone down," and crossed his throat with his finger and pointed to the sky. Said prosecutor Roy Amlot, QC:

The sister on duty, who arrived a few minutes later, was so concerned she informed her nursing service and the police were called the next day. A consultant in charge said he could not envisage a therapeutic reason for the combination of lignocaine and potassium. But at least two leading medical experts recently acknowledged that in the mid-1980s some hospitals, including where Lodwig trained, experimented with the mixture as a painkiller. This could mean Dr Lodwig's intention was to relieve the patient's pain and not to kill.

The relatives of Mr Spratley do not blame Dr Lodwig in any way. In these circumstances the crown has decided that without doubt the right course is to offer no further evidence.

Gilbert Gray, QC, defending, said, "There can be no doubt he tried to kill the pain, not the patient."

In commenting on the case in *The Independent* of 11 July 1989, journalist Peter Francis made the following points:

It is a case which involves very difficult moral and ethical problems as to the treatment of the terminally ill and what it was proper to do to relieve pain and suffering. He is a young doctor of exemplary character who finds himself the subject of this controversial and distressing charge at the outset of his career.

10

DAUGHTER HELPS MOTHER TO DIE
A case study from Wales

How can it be expected that a truly loving daughter could stand by and watch her mother, fatally ill with a crippling and painful disease, continue to suffer unnecessarily?

The loving daughter who helped her mother die by giving her drugs and putting a pillow over her face was put on probation at Cardiff court in July 1989. Mr Justice Mars Jones told Phillipa Managhan, 31, of Cardiff, "I think you have suffered enough. You are obviously a caring and loving person. You did what you did because you didn't want your mother to suffer."

The judge said that Phillipa's mother wanted to die and brought great emotional pressure to bear on her daughter to help her to terminate her life. "It was unlawful. I can show mercy and this I do. I am prepared to place you on probation." Phillipa was given two years probation on condition she attends Whitchurch Hospital. Phillipa said after her mother's death, "She's happy now. I had to do it. She made me do it. I promised I'd do it." Phillipa had pleaded guilty to attempting to murder her mother.

Mr John Williams, QC, for the prosecution said that in March 1986 Mrs Sylvia Williams was diagnosed as having motor neurone disease, a progressive condition which causes paralysis of the muscles but does not affect the brain. There is no known cure. Her doctor prescribed medicine to alleviate the symptoms. It included sleeping tablets. In ten months her health had got so bad that she needed constant attention. Phillipa had been living away from Cardiff, but now returned home to care for her mother. Mother and daughter were very attached to each other.

Mrs Williams became upset and depressed at the prospect of dying in hospital. In the summer of 1988 she started to talk of being helped to take her own life. She spent Christmas 1988 with another daughter in Scunthorpe and told her she wanted to die. By this time she was unable to take her own life as she did not have the use of her arms. She asked her daughter to promise that if necessary she would help her take an overdose. Mrs Williams made similar appeals to her other daughters, Penny and Elaine, as well as the defendant, Phillipa.

On 1 February she asked Phillipa to speak to an undertaker to discuss funeral arrangements. Her condition had gone from bad to worse and she had extreme difficulty in talking and making herself understood. On 27 February the family doctor called, finding her symptoms very distressing. She could hardly speak or swallow. Her limbs were virtually paralysed. The doctor decided she had very little time to live and discussed her admission to Rookwood Hospital in Cardiff.

On 8 March her home help noticed that Mrs Williams was crying and she said she had nothing to live for. In a few days all the daughters gathered together in Cardiff. The pain made it impossible for Mrs Williams to eat. Phillipa said to the home help that she might give her tablets in a few days, but did not feel sure she could go through with it. On 14 March Mrs Williams gave £400 to Phillipa to buy clothes for the funeral. On 15 March Phillipa visited the local priest and asked if God would forgive anyone who had helped someone to die. The priest told her it was wrong to kill anyone. On 16 March Mrs Williams spoke to all her daughters about dying. By early evening all had left except Phillipa. Elaine returned at 9.45 p.m. She was told to contact the others, and to keep out of the bedroom. When the other daughters arrived Phillipa said, "Mum's happy now."

Elaine went into the bedroom and there, Phillipa put her arms about her mother saying, "I had to do it. I loved her so much. I have made her happy for all of us now." Phillipa said she had put a pillow over her mother's face. She said her mother had been choking and she could not leave her like that. A doctor was called and pronounced Mrs Williams dead. Phillipa said she had placed a plastic bag over her mother's face and put a pillow over it.

Phillipa was interviewed by the police and admitted giving her mother about 60 tablets and trying to smother her. She explained how her mother had planned her death. Asked if she accepted responsibility, Phillipa replied, "Yes, Yes." She told the police, "I know it sounds silly, I didn't want my mum to die. I wanted her to stop suffering."

Forensic examination showed that the tablets would not have caused death. There was no evidence of injury anywhere on the external surface of the body. The judge said that "this lack of evidence is not inconsistent with the admission by the daughter that she placed a plastic bag and pillow over her mother's face." The Detective Inspector who investigated the case said that he became emotionally concerned for Phillipa and, he said, the picture she painted was so vivid that you were almost reliving the act again.

It cannot be said in this case that Phillipa encouraged her mother or showed herself to be eager to assist. The pressures upon her were enormous and these would be the more oppressive the more she loved and cared for her mother.

Can you imagine the guilt a loving daughter would feel if she had to watch the continual further and greater suffering of her mother after she had refused to help her to die. Imagine the different feelings of guilt if the same daughter did help her mother to die. What if later she saw others seemingly recovering or if there was found a new cure?

The daughter who cares enough to help a parent, as Phillipa did, is to be praised for her love, compassion, and courage, and not treated as if she were a common criminal.

11

SON IS JAILED FOR MANSLAUGHTER

Malcolm Ambrose killed his 85 year old father, who was dying a painful death, and was jailed for twelve months. Mr Justice Farquharson imposed the sentence after the 39 year old defendant said he would not feel that justice had been done if he was set free. He was still in a highly emotional state and had not come to terms with what had happened or with the loss of the one human being in the world he was close to, said Mr Escott Cox, defending in the Nottingham court hearing in January 1989.

Ambrose had pleaded not guilty to murder but guilty of manslaughter on the grounds of diminished responsibility. The defendant was of good character and well thought of. His mother had died nine years ago and he lived with his father who suffered from terminal cancer and severe bronchial pneumonia.

Professor Stephen Jones, the pathologist, was satisfied that the father would have died within three days if the son had not killed him. The cause of death was head injuries and asphyxia due to compression of the neck.

The deceased had seen his doctor recently and told him he wanted to die. Under medical advice he agreed to go to the Queens Medical Centre. It was the defendant who had cared for his father, and without that care his father could not have remained in the community as he was totally dependent on his son.

It appears that the deceased changed his mind and would not go into the hospital. Malcolm told the doctor he would continue to care for his father. At home his father kept a big hammer handy as protection against burglars. He handed this hammer to his son who struck eleven blows to his father's head. Malcolm then tried manual strangulation, called the police and said, "I have just murdered my father." He never mentioned "mercy killing."

12

THE CASE OF DR CARR
A legal landmark?

Although little notice was taken of this case it may turn out to be a landmark in the acceptance of euthanasia in Great Britain.

In August 1985, Ronald Mawson, aged 63, was dying of lung cancer. The disease had spread to the spine and brain and he had developed pneumonia. Pain was kept at bay by a cocktail of drugs every four hours, but he was breathless, restless and in great distress. The doctors differed as to whether he could live for three or four days or, at the most, three or four weeks.

Dr John Douglas Carr, who had been Mawson's friend and doctor for many years, was accused at his trial in Leeds of attempting to murder his patient because, in the doctor's own words, he "wished him to be allowed to die with dignity." No other motive was suggested. The charge was *attempted* murder, because death was in any case so near that the pathologist could not be sure that it had not resulted from the disease from which Mawson was suffering rather than from the injection of pheno-barbitone he had been given.

So far as we know, this is the first time in England that a charge has been laid against a doctor in circumstances of this kind.

The case was heard in Leeds in November 1986 and lasted fourteen days. The judge was Mr Justice Mars Jones. Mr Geoffrey Rivlin, QC represented the prosecution and Mr Bernard Hargrove QC the defence.

Dr Carr, aged 59, was described in court as a well-loved family doctor, practising on his own with a workload of 3500 patients. His children having grown up, he lived alone, working a 15-hour day with, as he said, "a free afternoon on Saturday to

44

do the shopping." When he first came to the practice he had to overcome the handicap of a very bad stammer. This still broke through occasionally when he was being questioned in the witness box, but for the most part was kept under control by an appliance known as the "Edinburgh masker" which, his counsel explained, prevented the stammerer from hearing his own voice. In the dock he listened intently, but his manner was relaxed and casual.

Witnesses testified to the confidence felt for him in the neighbourhood and its dependence upon him. When they heard he was to go on trial patients and neighbours had collected 3000 signatures to a petition in his support. In the words of the Methodist minister whose visits had often coincided with his own "He really enjoys being a community doctor."

Evidence was given of Dr Carr's special interest in the problems of the dying, in which his views were not always the same as those of the local hospice. The vice-chairman of the area Family Practitioner Committee said Dr Carr had "a special relationship with his patients, especially with the dying, who need his attention at any time." During his own evidence Dr Carr said reflectively "people find it very hard to accept the fact of death."

In the final speech for the prosecution, Mr Rivlin urged the jury not to acquit "a doctor minded to do this sort of thing because he has a bee in his bonnet."

Mr Justice Mars Jones, in summing up clearly hostile to the defence, said that euthanasia was against the law, whether with or without the patient's consent. "However gravely ill a man may be, however near his death, he is entitled in our laws to every hour, nay every minute of life that God has granted him. A doctor is not entitled to play God and cut short life because he believes the time has come to end the pain and suffering and to enable his patient to 'die with dignity'."

The jury twice returned to the court unable to reach a verdict. After a night in a hotel, they came back to a court house which, exceptionally, had been opened on a Saturday. There was a gasp of relief, and some quickly stiffled applause, at the verdict of Not Guilty. The judge refused costs to the defence, adding "I say no more." And the doctor returned to his patients.

13

MIXED THOUGHTS

Life is one long process of getting tired.
Samuel Butler

In those days men shall seek death, and shall not find it;
and shall desire to die, and death shall flee from them.
The Holy Bible

The following random thoughts may encourage a more thorough consideration of voluntary euthanasia.

Consider the sheer weight of personal evidence and experience. Visit old people's homes and hospices. See the victims of strokes and talk to the aged who live alone. The blood and the tears of the suffering call out for a dignified death so long denied.

Face up to the realities of terminal illness which often means cancer. Distress and loss of dignity can be severe and continuous. Often this means a living death. Many suffer breathlessness, incontinence, difficulty with speech or swallowing, vomiting, bedsores, tumours, etc. Think of the total loss of dignity to a patient who always needs another person to wipe his nose, or take him to the toilet, to change his sheets, to constantly clean his body. Surely it is better to die. Surely all caring people should support the Voluntary Euthanasia Society. The society aims to obtain legality for an adult person, suffering severe distress and pain from an incurable disease or illness, to receive medical help to die at their own considered request.

A severely ill patient was asked what was the best and worst part of his day. He replied that the best time was when he went to sleep, and the worst time was when he woke up.

In Holland, voluntary euthanasia is practised to some extent without penalty. No doctor is prosecuted as long as he keeps within the guidelines or conditions laid down. Not only the dying but the paralysed can be given aid in dying. The pioneering Dutch doctors have taken out of the suffering the long term dread.

Why keep alive those who do not want to live?

Dr Christian Barnard has said that he never saw anything ennobling about a writhing body. This answers those of religious zeal who contend that one is bettered and made more holy by suffering.

Here are the guidelines issued to doctors in Holland:

1. *There must be physical or mental suffering which the sufferer finds unbearable.*
2. *The suffering and the desire to die must not be temporary.*
3. *The decision to die must be the voluntary decision of an informed patient.*
4. *The patient must have a correct and clear understanding of his condition and prognosis. He must be capable of weighing the options open to him and must have done so.*
5. *There must be no other solution that is acceptable to the patient.*
6. *The time and manner of death must not cause avoidable misery to others (i.e. if possible the next of kin should be informed and the patient should put his affairs in reasonable order).*
7. *The decision to give aid-in-dying must not be a one-person decision. Consulting another professional is obligatory.*
8. *A medical doctor must be involved in the decision and in prescribing the correct drugs.*
9. *The decision process and the actual aid must be done with the utmost care.*
10. *The person receiving aid-in-dying need not be terminally ill, e.g. he or she could be paraplegic.*

A British Medical Association working party, in rejecting voluntary euthanasia, include this bit of humour:

We shall start by putting patients away because they are in intolerable pain and have not long to live anyway; we shall end by putting them away because its Friday night and we want to get away for the weekend.

The paucity of argument is quite tragic.

If voluntary euthanasia was legally permitted and doctors endorsed in their actions to provide a dignified death, would there be thousands calling for death to be made available? Not at all. Dutch doctors have said they deal with from one to three annually. Not exactly an avalanche!

A letter from a nurse tutor included the following:

Senior nurses often come into conflict with the medical profession over the question of treatment designed to prolong life without regard for the quality of life and, indeed, the wishes of the patient.

Recently Claire Raynor, made it known that she had made an advance directive. She said, "I'm making a living will which sets out the conditions under which I don't want to be kept alive."

Alan Pompidou, the son of the former president of France drafted the following euthanasia clause for a debate in the European Parliament:

In the absence of any possibility of cure, and after the failure of palliative care carried out correctly both medically and psychologically, whenever a patient who is fully conscious demands, in a pressing and continuous manner, that an end be put to an existence which has lost all dignity for him, and a panel of doctors specifically constituted for this purpose certifies that any further treatment is impossible, this demand may be satisfied, provided it does not involve any breach of respect for human life.

How not to be, that is the question.

14

A LETTER FROM A VES MEMBER
IN ENGLAND

My husband killed himself a few weeks ago. I hope that some of the people, especially MPs, who are so opposed to any consideration of legalising euthanasia will read this, and other more eloquent accounts of why and how this happens, and think again. Please.

He wasn't young – late 60s – and had been diagnosed as suffering from multiple sclerosis about ten years ago. Until then he had been in perfect health. From the early days of the diagnosis we agreed that suicide might eventually be the only escape route if his life threatened to become intolerable through total or near-total immobility. We both had, I have, strong moral convictions, which include the notion that one human right should be the right to decide the end of one's life.

The first years weren't bad, but in the last two he deteriorated a lot and became virtually house-bound, though still able to get about the house and to climb, labouriously, upstairs. Music and books remained the stimulus and solace they had always been. But about two months ago he got much worse and was no longer able to stand, or to turn over in bed without help. Blurred vision began.

The National Health Service were magnificent – district nurses visiting daily, equipment loaned, frequent visits by a caring doctor. I don't think we could have had better or more committed care if we had been able to put thousands of pounds on the table. But. It took about 15 minutes to help him from the bed, hastily installed downstairs, onto the wheelchair, then I wheeled him into the sitting room, then the tiring hoisting and heaving to get him onto a chair. Suppositories, commode, inspection for bed sores, constant fatigue, and the conviction that life as he knew it and defined it was finished. J (we'll call him that), had always said that life wasn't life without some control over your body, and now he could scarcely sit in a chair without slipping down. Enough was enough – to him, this would be an existence of physical humiliation, totally restricted activity and perhaps the prospect of life in hospital. He didn't want it, and I agreed. Yes, of course I admire the courage of those who go on, but J's courage was of a different sort.

We discussed it fully. His means of ending his life were of course very limited, but he had already decided on the course used a little earlier by Bettelheim – sedatives plus a plastic bag. He was very calm, cheerful too, in the last couple of days, and we talked a lot. He was absolutely determined. And I knew that for him *this was the right choice*. One little example – "I'll never take a book from the top shelf of a bookcase again" he said. But he spoke too of the pressure on an overworked and underfunded health service, and the fact that his days as a productive member of society were over. So those last days aren't a tragic or distressing memory. Not at all. But he stopped watching TV news or reading newspapers.

The first attempt failed – he fell asleep too soon. In the morning he said "But of course I'll try again." Then I realised that I wanted to help him – not to lie tense and sleepless upstairs, wondering. This was what he desperately wanted – a lonesome journey, but less so if someone is there at the end.

So this is how it was. We were both relaxed and calm and we talked for hours on the last day. Then the slow progress to bed. I didn't feel like crying except when he asked me to wash his feet. He didn't want them to be dirty when authority took over. But I didn't cry; it was too important and too charged with different emotions for that.

He made preparations with the bag, ready to pull down. Then he took the sedatives and said: "It's marvellous that you're here. Make sure I'm dead before you call anyone. I'm really glad to be leaving, though I'll miss you." The sedatives worked rather quickly and then I did the difficult bit. I don't want to use the actual words. He died quickly, very quickly, and the sense I had was of total peace. His hands lay on his chest and I sat with him for hours, literally for hours. Just after he died there seemed to be the slamming of a door, and a faint roll of thunder. There was nothing to be frightened by. I was so glad that I had shared and helped – how could I ever have thought (as I had) that I must not be involved.

I perjured myself at the inquest – I couldn't face going public, and this is the only part of it I feel ashamed of. I couldn't face the hassle. And I am angry, very angry that J had to act so furtively, with support only from me, none from society, in this decision. It isn't like that in Holland. And there it seems to be all right – no stories of people being nudged into death by greedy heirs. Of course there must be safeguards and there can be.

Were we wrong? I don't think so. Now there is a dull ache, but no regret – I'm glad he has escaped.

I respect the moral principles of other people – won't you respect mine and J's? Think again. Please.

15

A VIEW FROM THE HEMLOCK SOCIETY IN THE UNITED STATES OF AMERICA

The Hemlock Society with branches all over the United States speaks out strongly for voluntary euthanasia.

In their newsletter for October 1991, Peter Godwin MD says:

Making abortion illegal did not cause the problem to disappear, but simply drove it underground with disastrous results. The fact that euthanasia is illegal now also has undesirable consequences .... Organized medicine and many physicians are opposed to euthanasia. To many it is unthinkable that doctors who are trained to cure should be involved in killing. The slippery slope argument is that euthanasia will lead to the killing of the disabled, the mentally incompetent and the destitute. We accept passive euthanasia, that is the removal of life-support systems, with the knowledge that death will be the inevitable result, but over days or weeks. Yet, active euthanasia, which could produce the same result quickly and mercifully, is shunned.

I believe that euthanasia should be an open option for people with an incurable disease, who are suffering severely, with no prospect of relief and who choose to die. I want that option for my loved ones and I want it for myself.

16

SEVENTY-FIVE PER CENT FAVOUR THE RIGHT TO DIE

In 1989 the Voluntary Euthanasia Society commissioned NOP to carry out a random statistical survey. The chief question asked was:

Some people say that the law should allow adults to receive medical help to an immediate peaceful death if they suffer from an incurable physical illness that is intolerable to them, provided they have previously requested such help in writing. Please tell me whether you agree or disagree with this.

These are the same words as used in surveys in 1976 and 1985. During the 13 years the percentage of the population in agreement with the statement has risen from 69 per cent to 75 per cent. This result is similar to that in many other countries throughout the world.

The breakdown of the poll results shows little difference in sex or economic grouping. What did show was that the younger people tended to be more in favour of voluntary euthanasia than the older people interviewed. The highest vote in favour of voluntary euthanasia came from the South West. The lowest vote in favour was from Wales, the North West and East Anglia.

Members of *all* religious persuasions show a majority in favour of voluntary euthanasia. Roman Catholics show 68 per cent and the Church of England 78 per cent in favour.

The voting in favour is well founded if Roman Catholics are now voting in favour. The opposition of the Roman church has done more to hold back progress than any other group. The very strong majority voting in favour of voluntary euthanasia shows that once again the makers and reformers of our laws are ignoring the wishes of the people.

17

THE LAW IN GREAT BRITAIN

Despite public demand there is no legislation dealing specifically with mercy killing or voluntary euthanasia. However, some sections of existing acts are relevant.

The Homicide Act

The Homicide Act 1957 applies to England and Wales and (with minor differences) to Scotland.

Section 2. On Diminished Responsibility

(1) Where a person kills or is party to the killing of another, he shall not be convicted of murder if he was suffering from such abnormality of mind ... as subsequently to impair his mental responsibility for his acts and omissions in doing or being party to the killing ...

(3) A person but for this section would be liable, whether as principal or as accessary, to be convicted of murder shall be liable instead to be convicted of manslaughter ...

Section 4. On Suicide Pacts

(1) It shall be manslaughter and shall not be murder for a person acting in pursuance of a suicide pact between him and another to kill the other or to be party to the other being killed by a third party.

Mercy Killing

In their *Report of the Working Party on Offences Against the Person*, issued in August 1986, the Criminal Law Revision Committee suggested that as an alternative to a charge of murder, there should be a new offence which would apply to a person who from compassion kills another person who is or is believed by him to be (1) permanently subject to great bodily pain or suffering or (2) permanently helpless from bodily or mental incapacity or (3) subject to rapid and incurable bodily or mental degeneration. The proposal did not necessarily require the consent of the deceased and a maximum penalty of two years imprisonment was proposed. The suggestion was not pursued. In many cases of "mercy killing" however, the charge has been reduced to manslaughter under S.2 (1) and (3) of the Homicide Act.

Suicide Act 1961

Section 2

(1) A person who aids, abets, counsels or procures the suicide of another, or an attempt by another to commit suicide, shall be liable on conviction on indictment to imprisonment for a term not exceeding fourteen years.

(2) If on the trial of an indictment for murder or manslaughter it is proved that the accused aided, abetted, counselled or procured the suicide of the person in question, the jury may find him guilty of that offence.

In the case of *R. v McShane* (1977) it was established that an attempt at assistance, even though no suicide takes place, is also punishable under the act.

Prosecutions, which have to be authorised by the Director of Public Prosecutions, have been few. The usual penalty has been probation or a suspended sentence, though imprisonment is not unknown. In the McShane case the sentence was imprisonment for two years.

In view of S.2 (1) the legality of the Voluntary Euthanasia Society's booklet *A Guide to Self-Deliverance* was questioned and became the subject of a civil action brought by the Attorney General in April 1983. The judge then took the view that in some (though not all) circumstances, distribution would be punishable under the Criminal Law.

18

WORLDWIDE PROGRESS

The Voluntary Euthanasia Society of Scotland have issued a statement of their aims, as follows:

Dying, which should be a natural, dignified and peaceful end to life, is far too often a painful, prolonged and distressing process. Death is then a happy release. People fear dying in pain or being kept alive in such distressing circumstances that death would be preferable.

Modern technology makes it possible to prolong life when there is no hope of recovery. It is therefore important to establish a person's right to decline artificial prolongation of life, and to meet death without pain, and with dignity.

To achieve this, members of euthanasia societies can make a form of declaration in writing and before witnesses, and in advance, that if there is no reasonable prospect of recovery from intolerable suffering and distress, they wish to be kept free from pain and do not want their lives prolonged by artificial means.

Nothing in this is unlawful. A card can be carried which summarises their advance declaration.

The long term aim is to bring about a change in the law so that active voluntary euthanasia can be undertaken.

Ludovic Kennedy has written about statistics on death: one person in five will die of cancer, thousands will die in severe and unrelieved pain. He says that either he or his readers or his or their relatives may well be among those who have to end their days in misery. He asks why they cannot be given a quick-acting pill to put them out of their misery. Why not euthanasia? Ludovic

58

Kennedy makes it clear he does not mean mercy killing of one person by another – rather that everyone should be allowed to fill in a form declaring that they do not want their life prolonged when it is no longer worth living. Such a written wish would make things easier for the doctors concerned.

All hospitals, says Mr Kennedy, should have under lock and key a lethal pill for use when a patient cannot stand any longer to be kept alive in terrible pain. Mr Kennedy tackles the objections – especially that voluntary euthanasia would lead to compulsory euthanasia – we agree that such fears are a nonsense. It must be remembered that it is the quality of life that matters and not its length.

The Voluntary Euthanasia Society of Scotland quotes the views of the Episcopal Bishop of St Andrews, Michael Hare Duke:

Why should we not allow the thread of life to be cut when it no longer links us meaningfully to a contemporary surrounding? If I do not know who I am, if I become an intolerable burden upon those who care about me or for me, would it not be better if I went my own way? I can find no fundamental theological argument which can justify human initiative in saving life but deny the right to make a judgement which says "no" to a life's continuance when compassion demands that a person should be released.

Recently an attempt to legalise doctor-assisted suicide in the USA very narrowly failed to become law.

In Japan a 34 year old doctor gave a lethal injection to a patient. The patient's family had begged the medical staff to stop treatment. The doctor withdrew treatment and gave the lethal dose in the presence of a relative. Police are investigating. The Japanese Society for Dying With Dignity thinks that Japan is not yet ready for active euthanasia. But passive euthanasia is accepted, allowing terminally ill patients the right not to be given treatment to keep them alive.

In the Netherlands it is still illegal to perform euthanasia or to assist suicide. However, if doctors do so according to guidelines they are not prosecuted. The government is sanctioning what is already happening.

In Canada it is a criminal offence to help anyone to commit suicide. In British Columbia a pharmacologist and cabinet minister admitted that he and his family had taken turns to give morphine to their father. This might have hastened death. He spoke out to get a discussion going. In a poll 75 per cent of Canadians favoured mercy killing of incurably ill patients if they had requested such in writing. The Canadian Medical Association condones passive euthanasia.

It is common in many countries, including France, to give patients an overdose if terminally ill. In 1991 the cancer specialist Leon Schwartzenberg was in trouble for declaring that he had helped some of his terminally ill patients to die.

In Australia both the medical fraternity and the public are moving more in favour of euthanasia. Two thousand doctors surveyed showed 869 in favour of voluntary euthanasia. One third said they had been involved at least once. Nearly half said they would practice voluntary euthanasia if it was legal.

In Germany active euthanasia is regarded as a crime punishable by up to five years in prison. Passive euthanasia has been overlooked, and the doctor left to decide when applicable. Suicide and assisting suicide are not forbidden by law.

In the USA a recent federal law requires that adult patients should be informed of their right to refuse life-sustaining medical treatment. Seventy per cent of people who die in hospital have had life-sustaining treatment withdrawn.

In Britain, euthanasia is bound to be on the parliamentary agenda before long.

As all over the world the call for voluntary euthanasia gains support, let us obey Shakespeare lest we miss the boat:

There is a tide in the affairs of man,
Which, taken at the flood, leads on to fortune;
Omitted, all the voyage of their life
Is bound in shallows and in miseries,
On such a full sea we are now afloat,
And we must take the current when it serves,
Or lose our ventures.

19

FINAL THOUGHTS AND FEELINGS

Adversity doth best discover virtue.
Francis Bacon

This is the doctrine, loved by religious fanatics, which has been taught for years to make man satisfied with his lot, however poor or miserable. The time has come to dispel this nonsense once and for all. There is no virtue in suffering, and even less in *unnecessary* suffering. No human being or animal should be expected to go on suffering when there is no hope of relief. No one should be required to lose their dignity and to become utterly dependent on others for every little thing. The only virtue to arise from suffering is the caring and the love shown by others to those suffering.

Shakespeare, in Measure for Measure causes the Duke to say:

> *If I must die,*
> *I will encounter darkness as a bride,*
> *And hug it in my arms.*

Many feel that they would welcome death. That the night of not knowing would come as a welcome relief from the wakening feelings of pain and despair. Death is a deliverance when life is not worth living. As Bentley remarked:

> *There is a great deal to be said*
> *For being dead.*

Byron's line "So abject – yet alive" expresses the condition of many to whom death must be a deliverance, gratefully welcomed.

The lines of Arthur Hugh Clough express exactly what those who call for voluntary euthanasia would like to be noted and acted upon by doctors:

> *Thou shalt not kill, but need'st not strive*
> *Officiously to keep alive.*

This officious striving to keep alive at all costs is the very behaviour that the terminally ill dislike and despair of. To relieve from continual pain and suffering by allowing death to take place is the course very much to be applauded.

"Age is full of care" wrote Shakespeare. There is no doubt of the truth of this observation. For this reason, and in gratitude for the love shown by the aged in their earlier years, we all should do what we can to ease the path of the older people. The loving young mother becomes an old lady, and some of the love given should be returned. Especially is this true when the older person is very ill, and suffering without let up. Age is full of care but this care can be lessened by loving kindness and consideration, and by the law responding to pleas to allow voluntary euthanasia when there is no hope of recovery from terminal illness.

"Death after life doth greatly please," wrote Edmund Spenser. If life is reduced to constant torture and absolute dependence on others then death might indeed be welcome. Let nobody forbid this welcome friend to those who suffer.

Coleridge speaks of death coming "with friendly care" and so it must be to many who can no longer tolerate the living death to which they have been subjected by a cruel fate. How can such relief be forbidden or delayed? Let no one strive unnecessarily to keep alive.

Said Donne, "Death is but a groom." What a lovely thought for those desiring relief from a burdensome life. To be guided away from pain and dependence into an oblivion where there is no pain. Browne remarked that "Death is the cure of all diseases." Laws that forbid euthanasia deny the cure that many cry for. I say again, let death come when it comes as a relief and a blessing. "Death is the end of woes," as Spenser said. Poets are people who allow the mind to wander and search for meanings in life, and over and over again, the greatest poets extol the virtue of death coming to one for whom life holds no more appeal.

Returning to the beginning. There is no argument. The mind must agree with voluntary euthanasia for the suffering who have no hope for a recovery or cure. There is no sustainable argument to make such people continue to suffer. There is no argument. That is, the mind is convinced.

But how do we feel?

When I took a much-loved dog to be put to sleep after he had gone mad and bitten me badly, I knew in my mind that I was doing the right thing. For the dog and for the people around that he might hurt. There was no sustainable argument against. But my feelings? I suffered agonies then, and for a long time after. Tears swelled in my eyes when I thought of what I had done to my best friend. I had him killed. There was no argument against, but I felt the most terrible guilt.

How much more then with a human being? There is no argument to convince the mind that voluntary euthanasia is correct in the circumstances but how do I feel? If I hand those extra pills to my beloved wife or daughter how will I feel? Probably everytime I think of her I will suffer the most awful sorrow and guilt. Yet I know I will have done right.

No one who loves can lightly put the loved one to death. That is why the suggestion that there is some evil in helping a loved one to die is insupportable. No one could do this without a great deal of heart searching. If one is prepared, for the good of the loved one, to suffer the pangs of conscience, perhaps for years, there is no ground upon which accusations of murder or manslaughter can be brought.

To persecute a loving being for an act of love is a terrible thing, and all nations and governments who do so are to be condemned.

One knows that any action to relieve the unending pain and misery of a loved one must be justified. To fight back one's feelings which would deny the action is a special kind of courage in action. To then have to endure the condemnation of one's peers is unforgivable.

In several of the case histories quoted in this book, and in many other writings on the subject of euthanasia, one thing stands out without exception. This is the reluctance to do what the sufferer desires. In several cases it is only after much heart searching and torment that the relative or friend finally helps the loved one to die. It is not easy to do. When done, to have to suffer accusations of evil is unforgivable.

Of course, it should not be necessary for loved ones to have to take this awful task, this terrible responsibility, upon themselves. The law should allow, with necessary safeguards, that the medical profession can end a life when there is no hope of recovery. I think all sick people, while in a good mental state, should say they wish to die with dignity ... but in a civilised society there should be no need for this. It should be understood that no human being will be left to suffer unnecessarily, and all have the right to a quick and dignified death to take away the awful half-life existence which is so demoralising.

Thinking back to my beloved dog ... I would have found it very difficult to take my dog's life myself even knowing it to be for the best. I did not have to. All I had to do was hand over the animal to a professional who did the deed. Likewise, it should not be left to relatives and friends to take life even in those circum-stances which totally justify such action. The professionals should be authorised to allow death to bring relief. While it continues to be illegal for doctors to do what they should be able to do, the loving and caring ones among us will have to do what is needed to help our loved ones to escape unnecessary suffering.

There is no argument.

20

OTHER BOOKS TO READ

The following books are recommended by the Voluntary Euthanasia Society in London.

Voluntary Euthanasia

Voluntary Euthanasia: Experts Debate the Right to Die A. B. Downing and Barbara Smoker (editors), published by Peter Owen, London. The most authoritative and comprehensive work that has been published in Great Britain.

The End of Life: Euthanasia and Morality James Rachel, published by Oxford University Press. A clear, reasoned argument for legalising euthanasia.

Good Life, Good Death Christian Barnard, published by Peter Owen, London. A courageous and easy to read declaration of faith by one of the few internationally known medical figures who has publically proclaimed the case for voluntary euthanasia.

Whose Life is it Anyway? Brian Clark, published by Samuel French, London. The famous play about a paralysed man confined to a hospital bed, and his struggle for personal autonomy.

Euthanasia: The Good Death Ludovic Kennedy, published by Chatto & Windus, London.

Suicide

Suicide and Attempted Suicide G. Stengel, published by Penguin Books, London.

Suicide and Deliberate Self-Harm Office of Health Economics, London, 1981.

The Savage God: A Study of Suicide Al Alvarez, published by Penguin Books, London.

Death and Dying

Dying John Hinton, published by Penguin Books, London.

Death and the Family Lily Pincus, published by Faber & Faber, London.

On Death and Dying Elizabeth Kubler-Ross, published by Tavistock Publications, London.

The Hospice Movement

The Hospice Movement Sandol Stoddard, published by Jonathan Cape, London.

Tears and Smiles: The Hospice Handbook 1990 Martin Lewis, published by Michael O'Mara, London.

Ageing

Ageing for Beginners Mary Stott, published by Blackwell Publishers, Oxford.

The Third Age Muriel Skeet, published by Darton Longman &
Todd, London. A guide for elderly people, their families and
friends.

Books Available from the Hemlock Society
See address in next chapter.

Let Me Die Before I Wake Derek Humphrey. The bible of the
euthanasia movement, revised in 1991. Printed in large type.
Personal struggles and family dilemmas are illustrated by true
stories. "A book which must be handled with care ..." *Los
Angeles Times* "A restrained but highly graphic book detailing
effective and relatively painless methods of 'delivering' the
terminally ill from pain-wracked life to death." *San Fransisco
Examiner*

Final Exit Derek Humphrey. Covers the practicalities of self-deliverance and assisted suicide for the dying and includes special
section for physicians and nurses. Aimed at mature adults who have
irreversible illness and are considering the option of rational
suicide if and when the pain becomes unbearable. The way in
which doctors and nurses may need to handle a patient's request
for euthanasia is outlined. Dr Frederick R. Abrams, physicist and
ethicist, says: "Derek Humphrey has condensed fifteen years of
exploring the issue of euthanasia in an honest, clear, compelling
book for those who seek the knowledge that will assure them a
good way through this final passage should it become necessary."

Last Wish Betty Rollin. Her prognosis hopeless, wracked with
pain, 76 year old Ida Rollin was dying of cancer. She made a
decision. Suicide. She asked her daughter for help. "This book
is not really about death. It is, instead, a loving tribute to Mrs
Rollin's spirited progress through life." *The Baltimore Sun* "One
of the most remarkable testaments of our time. It makes you want
to embrace the writer for her courage." *Cosmopolitan*

Is This the Day? Vilma Hollingbery. A powerful, uncompromising love story. Confronts euthanasia. A play commissioned by the Royal Theatre, Northampton, England.

Jean's Way Derek Humphrey. Planned self-deliverance from terminal cancer with help from her husband. "A rare and marvellous book about somebody who made the most of the end of her life, who got fulfillment and joy out of her dying years." *Daily Mail*

Double Exit Ann Wickett. A moving example of an elderly couple choosing to die together, and an examination of scores of similar cases.

Common Sense Suicide Doris Portwood. A classic in its field, covering the history and psychology of suicide.

The Right to Die Derek Humphrey and Ann Wickett. Gives a very thorough history of euthanasia beginning with Greek and Roman attitudes to death. Considers medical and legal issues as well as the moral and ethical questions. "It is hard to understand why one should postpone death when one is no longer enjoying life." B. F. Skinner, Harvard University.

Euthanasia and Religion Gerald A. Laurie. A survey of the attitudes of world religions to the right to die.

21

VES ADDRESSES

Australia

South Australia Voluntary Euthanasia Society P.O. Box 2151, Kent Town Centre, 5071, South Australia.

Voluntary Euthanasia Society of New South Wales P.O. Box 25, Broadway, NSW 2007

Voluntary Euthanasia Society of Victoria Box 108, Mooroolbark, 3138 Victoria

West Australia Voluntary Euthanasia Society P.O. Box 7243, Cloisters Square, Perth, W. Australia 6000

Belgium

Association pour le Droit de Mourir dans le Dignite 55 Rue de President, B-1050, Bruxelles

Recht op Waaridg Sterven Constitutlestraat 33, 2008 Antwerpen

Canada

Dying With Dignity 175 St Clair Avenue West, Toronto, Ontario M4VlP7

Fondation Responable Jusqu'a la Fin 10150 De Bretagne, Quebbec (Neufchatel), PQ G2B 2R1

Colombia

Fundacion Pro Derecho a Morir Dignamente 88900, Bogata

Denmark

Landsforeningen Mit Livstestamente Brondstrupvej 5, 8500 Grena

France

Association pour le Droit de Mourir dans la Dignite 103 Rue Lafayette, 75010, Paris

Great Britain

The Voluntary Euthanasia Society 13 Prince of Wales Terrace, London W8 5PG

The Voluntary Euthanasia Society of Scotland 17 Hart Street, Edinburgh

India

The Society for the Right to Die With Dignity 127 Mahatma Gandhi Road, Bombay 400 023

Israel

The Israeli Society for the Right to Die With Dignity 116 Rothschild Bolv., Tel Aviv 65271

Japan

Japan Society for Dying With Dignity Watanabe Bdg., 202, 2-20-1 Hongou, Bunkyoku, Tokyo 113

Luxembourg

Association pour le Droit de Mourir dans la Dignite 50 Bd. Kennedy, 4170 Esch-Alzette

Netherlands

Nederlandse Vereniging voor Vrijwillige Euthanasie 152 de Lairessestraat Postbus 5331 1007 AH Amsterdam

Stichting Landelijk Besluithuis Zuiderweg 42, 8293 KT Vinkega, Fri

New Zealand

Voluntary Euthanasia Society (Auckland) Inc P.O. Box 3709, Auckland

Voluntary Euthanasia Society 95 Melrose Road, Island Bay, Wellington 2

South Africa

South Africa Voluntary Euthanasia Society P.O. Box 1460, Wandsbeck 3631

Spain

Asociacon Derecho a Moir Dignimante Apartado 31, 134, 08080 Barcelona

Sweden

Ratten Till Var Dod Hoganasgatan 2 C.753 30 Uppsala

Switzerland

EXIT Association por de Droit de Mourir dans la Dignite C.P. 100, CH-1222 Vesenaz, Geneva

EXIT (Deutsche Schweiz) Vereinigung fur humanes Sterben CH-2540 Grenchen

United States of America

Americans Against Human Suffering, Inc. P.O. Box 11001, Glendale, CA 91206

Concern for Dying 250 West 57th Street, Rm 831, New York, NY 10107

The National Hemlock Society P.O. Box 11830, Eugene, OR 97440

Society for the Right to Die 250 West 57th Street, New York, NY 10107

22

ADVANCE DIRECTIVE

TO MY FAMILY, MY PHYSICIAN AND ALL OTHER PERSONS CONCERNED

THIS DIRECTIVE is made by me _____

_____

_____

at a time when I am of sound mind and after careful consideration.

I DECLARE that if at any time the following circumstances exist, namely:

(1)   I suffer from one or more of the conditions mentioned in the schedule; and

(2)   I have become unable to participate effectively in decisions about my medical care; and

(3)   two independent physicians (one a consultant) are of the opinion that I am unlikely to recover from illness or impairment involving severe distress or incapacity for rational existence,

THEN AND IN THOSE CIRCUMSTANCES my directions are as follows:

1   that I am not to be subjected to any medical intervention or treatment aimed at prolonging or sustaining my life;

2   that any distressing symptoms (including any caused by lack of food or fluid) are to be fully controlled by appropriate analgesic or other treatment, even though that treatment may shorten my life.

I consent to anything proposed to be done or omitted in compliance with the directions expressed above and absolve my medical attendants from any civil liability arising out of such acts or omissions.

I wish it to be understood that I fear degeneration and indignity far more than I fear death. I ask my medical attendants to bear this statement in mind when considering what my intentions would be in any uncertain situation.

I RESERVE the right to revoke this DIRECTIVE at any time, but unless I do so it should be taken to represent my continuing directions.

SCHEDULE

A   Advanced disseminated malignant disease.

B   Severe immune deficiency.

C   Advanced degenerative disease of the nervous system.

D   Severe and lasting brain damage due to injury, stroke, disease or other cause.

E   Senile or pre-senile dementia, whether Alzheimer's, multi-infarct or other.

F   Any other condition of comparable gravity.

Signed _____

Date _____

WE TESTIFY that the above-named signed this Directive in our presence, and made it clear to us that he/she understood what it meant. We do not know of any pressure being brought on him/her to make such a directive and we believe it was made by his/her own wish. So far as we are aware we do not stand to gain from his/her death.

Witnessed by:

Signature: _____   Signature: _____

Name: _____   Name: _____

Address: _____   Address: _____

_____   _____

_____   _____

Issued by the Voluntary Euthanasia Society, 13 Prince of Wales Terrace, London W8 5PG

INDEX